Our family got a stepparent

Carolyn E. Phillips

Regal Books A Division of G/L Publications
Ventura, CA U.S.A.

Other books by Carolyn Phillips:
Our Family Got a Divorce
Michelle

The foreign language publishing of all Regal Books is under the direction of Gospel Literature International (GLINT). GLINT provides financial and technical help for the adaptation, translation and publishing of books for millions of people worldwide. For more information regarding translation, contact: GLINT, P.O. Box 6688, Ventura, California 93006.

Published by Regal Books
A Division of GL Publications
Ventura, California 93006
Printed in U.S.A.

Library of Congress Cataloging in Publication Data
Phillips, Carolyn E.
   Our family got a stepparent.

   Summary: A young boy relates how, with God's help, he adjusted to his stepfather and the changes in his life caused by his mother's remarriage.
   1. Stepparents—United States—Juvenile literature.
[1. Stepparents. 2. Remarriage. 3. Christian life]
I. Title.
HQ759.92.P48   306.8'7   81-51275
ISBN 0-8307-0786-7 (pbk.)   AACR2

To our very own stepfather
who has loved us
into a real family.
Thank you, Dad.

Introduction

Ask any stepkid you know and he'll probably tell you that being a stepchild isn't very easy. You've gotta learn how to share your house, your life and your very own *parent* with someone you hardly even know; maybe even a couple of new someones if you marry *their* kids too.

But being a stepparent isn't easy either, even at best. Walking cold into a ready-made family is a little like being asked to make an impromptu speech to the combined assembly of the House and Senate—everybody *but you* knows how things are done.

OUR FAMILY GOT A STEPPARENT is about the unique blend of people and circumstances found in stepfamilies. If you have "steps" in your family, this little book is for you, to make some of the happenings that occur in your family easier to talk about and, therefore, easier to deal with.

Each chapter deals with a separate subject or concern—real or imagined—to children of stepfamilies. And Chip tells his reader things that should prepare you to discuss *your own* feelings together. Some topics may seem familiar to you, others may be things you've never dealt with. In either case, if you end up *talking together,* Chip has done what he came for.

We wish you love and godspeed in your pilgrimage through life—hand in hand as a whole family.

Contents

Chapter One
Enough Love for Me?

Grown-ups sure are hard to figure out! My real Mom and Dad were awful unhappy together so they got a divorce even though I didn't like it. I was all mixed up about it. But we talked a lot and Mom and Dad listened to how I felt. Just talking about it helped a lot.

After the divorce I still wanted my Mom and Dad to get married again. I even pretended that they really loved each other—like before. But what did happen is that my Dad married this other lady called Linda. She teaches school. Third grade.

After a while living with just my Mom wasn't so bad. At least Sis and I didn't have to share her with anybody. It was like she loved us better than anybody else. But sometimes Mom went out with some of her lady friends—and sometimes even with a man.

When Mom went out we had a neat baby-sitter (I don't know why they call her a *baby*-sitter. We aren't babies!). Carol's a big girl from down the street. She comes and plays games with us and tells us neat stories. It's fun when Carol's around.

But I got mixed up all over again when Mom started dating. I asked her, "If we love each other so much, how come you go out with other people?"

"Honey," Mom said, brushing her hair slowly, "I love you and Sis more than anybody in the whole world. But it's important for me to spend time with grown-ups too—men and women." Then she laid her hairbrush on the dresser and hugged me and said, "Nobody will ever take your place."

One Friday night after Mom got home from work, this man came to the door. He was all dressed up in a suit and everything. And Mom smiled real wide when she saw him. She brought the man in and told us his name was Bill. He smiled at me and Sis and shook my hand. He said he'd heard a bunch of stuff about us. Then Carol came and Mom and Bill left for the restaurant.

Next morning at breakfast I was putting jam on a piece of toast. "Mom," I said without looking at her, "are you gonna marry Bill?"

"I don't know, Chip," she said, pouring more coffee into her cup. "I like Bill very much. He's a nice person. But I don't know him well enough to be thinking about marrying him. That will take a long time."

We saw Bill a lot after that 'cause he went to our church and he came over whenever he could. Part of me liked him a bunch. He was funny and nice to Sis and me. And most of the time he really listened to us. Lots of times they took Sis and me places with them. We went to the zoo, and took a train trip for a whole day once.

But part of me didn't like Bill very much at all. What if he did marry my mom? What would happen then? Mom and Sis and me were doing just fine on our own. We loved each other. We didn't need Bill coming in and taking all of Mom's love for himself!

Saturday morning I was at Gram's (my grandmother). We were "resting" from pulling weeds in her flower garden. I was cutting me a piece of apple pie while Gram poured lemonade in some glasses for us.

"Gram," I said, licking the sweet apple juice from my fingers, "how much love does a person have?"

"To keep?" she asked. "Or to give away?"

"To give away, I guess," I said, sitting in one of the wooden chairs across the table from her. "I mean, how many people can you love before you run out of love to give 'em?"

"Well," Gram said, sipping her lemonade slowly, "love isn't like the pie you cut. When you cut the last piece off that pie, it's gone."

"Right."

"But love isn't like that. In fact it's just backwards. The more you give love away, the more you have. It's *made* to be given away. If we *don't* give love to people, it turns into selfishness—love only for ourselves."

I stuck another bite of pie in my mouth and thought while I chewed. "You mean when you give love away it makes *more* love?"

"That's what I mean," Gram said, smiling. "Grown-ups and kids can love lots of different people."

I still didn't want to have to share Mom with anybody else, but in case I ever had to, it was good to know there just might be enough love to go around.

Chapter Two
And What About Dad?

It was almost Christmas! One night after dinner Mom and Bill were sitting on the floor with Sis and me helping us wrap presents for our friends. I got a new baseball for Pete 'cause we'd played with his so much the cover was coming off. He was really gonna be surprised!

Mom finished tying a big bow on one of my sister's packages. Then she sat up real straight and took a deep breath. "You kids are working so hard on surprises for your friends," she said. "How would you like a surprise that Bill and I have for you?" She looked at both of us and smiled. "How would you kids like to have Bill for a stepdad?"

I almost swallowed the Christmas sticker I was licking. I looked at Sis. She was sitting there with a dumb grin on her face. Bill was OK to have around but I didn't want anything to do with having a stepfather. It was OK for Linda to be my stepmother, 'cause I didn't have to see her very much. But it would be different if Bill married Mom. He'd *live* with us! In the same house and everything! I didn't like that idea at all!

"Chip?" Mom was looking at me. "You haven't said anything."

"Things are just fine the way they are!" I said without looking at anybody. "We don't need to change."

I peeked a quick look at Mom. Her eyes looked sad. But *I* didn't *want* a stepfather. *I already had a dad!* I didn't need another one.

The Christmas carols played on the radio the rest of the evening while we popped popcorn. (It was supposed to be for stringing but we ate more than we put on the tree.) Everybody was nice, smiling and stuff, but underneath there was a kind of sadness.

When Mom came into my room later to say goodnight, I hugged her extra long. Mom always smells good. "Mom," I whispered, "I don't want anybody to take Dad's place."

"Is that what you're worried about?" Mom asked, sitting down on my bed beside me. "Bill isn't going to take your dad's place. He'll be a new and *different* person in your life. Someone else you'll learn to get along with, maybe even learn to love."

"I'm never gonna love *anybody* more than I love my dad!"

"And nobody wants you to try," Mom said, getting up and fixing the covers. She kissed my cheek and turned out the light.

I just stared at the dark ceiling for a little while, thinking about getting a stepdad, and thinking about my real dad. I missed him a lot.

After a while I rolled over on my side so I could see the stars through the window. "God?" I said quietly, "you there? I guess Bill's gonna be my stepdad, even if I don't like it. Make it work out OK, 'cause I'm scared."

Chapter Three
But You Don't Even Know My Mom!

It was fun shopping for the rest of our presents and hanging red and green decorations everywhere. This year I got to set up the manger scene all by myself. The whole house smelled like Christmas trees. I couldn't help feeling excited. It was like magic. The only thing wrong was that my dad wasn't there, too. I missed him awful bad at Christmas time. And this year things were gonna be *real* different. We were having *three days of celebrating*!

Two days before Christmas Sis and I drove to another town with Dad and Linda to spend that day celebrating. We met all the new grandparents and cousins. Linda had a *big* family.

It was scary, meeting all those strangers at once. They were nice and everything, but Sis and I stuck pretty close to Dad. I think he was a little worried, too. There were people there he never met before, either.

Linda's tiny little grandma was there. (I didn't know big people even *had* grandmas.) She had white hair and couldn't hear good but it was fun to listen to her stories. She told about when she was a little girl. She had a horse all her own.

There was a bunch of kids there, too. They were all cousins with each other. One of the babies sure cried a lot.

Everybody hugged everybody else when it was time for us to go. And Linda's Aunt Sue wanted me and Sis to kiss her good-by. Sis hid behind Dad and Aunt Sue just laughed, but I had to kiss her cheek. She smelled like flowers. I sure was glad when we were in the car on our way back home.

It was late at night and Sis was asleep in the front seat. So I stretched out on the back seat and watched the shadowy trees going past the window. I was sleepy but I couldn't stop thinking about what I heard Grandma Williams and one of Linda's aunts saying in the kitchen. They didn't know I could hear them, and I wasn't sneaking, either. They just didn't hear me when I came in the room.

Grandma Williams was saying what a nice man my dad was. That made me feel real good. I wanted everybody to like my dad. But then the other lady said she was glad my dad married Linda. She said Sis and me needed a good mother.

I don't understand why anyone would say something like that. My mom is the best mother in the whole world . . . and I love her. I thought and thought about what they said.

When we got home Dad carried Sis into the house and Linda and I unloaded our presents from the trunk. They gave me a neat model airplane that can really fly, and three new games. And they gave Sis a doll house with tiny furniture and a whole family of little dolls, even a baby. And then they gave us each a whole $10 bill to spend any way we want to.

After we set the stuff down inside the door, I watched Dad and Linda get back in their car and drive away. I stood at the window for a while, even after I couldn't see them anymore.

Then Mom put her arm around my shoulder and—I didn't mean to, but I started to cry. "What's wrong, honey?" Mom asked me, sitting on the arm of the couch. "Did something happen? Tell me what's wrong."

"Nothing happened," I said, but I couldn't stop the tears.

"Chip," Mom said quietly, "I want to help, but I can't if you won't tell me what's going on."

"I heard some ladies talking at Linda's house," I blurted out, "and they said they were glad Dad married Linda . . . 'cause Sis and me needed a good mother."

I could feel Mom sit up straighter and I looked up at her. Her face looked mad, like a fist. And for a couple of minutes she didn't say anything. When she looked at me I could see there were tears in her eyes. "Honey," she said, "I would give anything to keep you from hearing mean things about the people you love. But that's something I can't control. Sometimes when people are angry or hurt they say unkind things about someone else.

"You and I know each other better than anybody else. That means you can *tell* when someone is saying what is true. If you're not sure about something, you come and ask me. We can talk about things anytime."

"But they don't even *know* you," I said. I felt mad inside at those ladies for what they said.

Mom hugged me real tight and said, "As long as *you* know I'm a good Mom, what anybody else thinks doesn't even count."

"Mom," I said, hugging her, "you're the very best Mom in the whole world. Those ladies would love you just like I do if they knew you like I do." I looked at her face, and she was smiling again. "You know what?" I asked.

"What?"

"I feel sorry for those ladies."

Chapter Four
More *New Relatives!*

The next day we had our Christmas with Bill's family. We ate at a nice restaurant on the way. We were having a good time. Bill said his family was excited about meeting all of us. I told him I was just scared about it. He laughed and then he told us some things about his mother and father from when he was a boy my age.

They used to live in the country and they raised fruit trees, like peaches and plums. He said his mom used to can the real ripe peaches for them to eat in wintertime and he had a special job. He got to tap all the jars on their new lids to see if they were sealed right. His mom canned a whole bunch of fruit like that so he had a whole lot of jars to tap on top. Things sure were different in the olden days.

We got to Bill's parents' house pretty quick and they all came out to the car to help carry packages inside and to meet and hug everybody.

They had a *real nice* house with different things sitting all around. There was a big statue of a dog on the fireplace. I didn't know it was a statue 'till I touched it. Everything matched in the whole house. At first I sat real still so I wouldn't break anything. I tried to be quiet and say "thank you" and "please" a bunch so they'd think Bill was getting some nice kids when he got married.

Bill's mother and father—we called them "Grandma and Grandpa Mac," short for Mackenzie—gave Sis and me some real nice presents. Sis got a baby doll in a basket. Grandma Mac made all the clothes and the whole basket herself. And Grandpa Mac made me something really special to go with the train set they gave me. He made a board with mountains and roads and trees on it. Then Grandpa Mac and Bill and me worked on putting one of the little buildings together before we had dinner. They were real nice people. They laughed a lot and I felt like I belonged there.

On the way home Sis was asleep next to me with her new doll. I was sitting in the back seat watching the houses pass by. I got to thinking. In two days I had gotten a whole lot of new relatives that I hardly even knew. New aunts and uncles and a bunch of new cousins. (I'll never learn all their names.) And so many grandmas and grandpas that we have to call them "Grandma Mac" and "Grandma Williams" to keep them all straight.

Some kids don't have *any* grandparents or cousins, and I've got 'em in bunches! I guess I'm really pretty lucky.

Chapter Five
What a Christmas!

Finally we got to Christmas Day and our *real* Christmas. At least it seemed like the only real Christmas to me. All the others were with people we didn't even know. Hugging and kissing people I never saw before. I like it when Gram and our regular aunts and uncles are there. I know what's gonna happen with them. I feel comfortable.

Santa brought Sis and me new bathrobes and a book. I thought he forgot my mitt but then I found a note from him in my stocking. It told me to go look in the refrigerator. I did and I found *another* note that told me to go look in the bathtub. When I looked in the tub I found a big box wrapped in red and green paper. My mitt was inside! I'm sure glad nobody took a shower before I found it.

Pretty soon the turkey was smelling good and Gram and my Aunt Ruth, my cousin Paul and my new Uncle Steve came. They brought pies and other stuff and they went into the kitchen with Mom. Paul and I could hear them laughing and talking while we worked on my train buildings on the rug. They were talking about the visits we made to everybody's houses and the presents everybody got. And Mom started to sound different, not happy anymore.

"He knows *I* can't afford to give them much," she said. "It makes me feel guilty and jealous. I feel like he's trying to buy the kids away from me."

I couldn't tell for sure, but it sounded like Mom was starting to cry. Bill hadn't given us his presents yet. He was going to do that today. Mom must be talking about Dad! I wondered if she was going to take away my model that really flies. I think it's neat. My *dad* gave it to me!

I didn't feel much like working on my train building anymore, so I put everything back in the little box. My big ol' dog Max was sleeping by the Christmas tree and when I walked by he followed me up the stairs to my room.

I set the box on my desk and sat there looking out the window. When today started it was great! Now all the happiness was gone. Why did that old divorce and the bad feelings have to stay around all the time? Why can't everybody just get along?

Paul came in and sat down on my bed. We just looked at each other. Then he said, "It's sad when your mom hurts." I just nodded my head up and down. "I remember when my mom would cry and stuff after our divorce," he said. "I felt all sick inside. It scared me. I didn't think Moms were supposed to cry."

"Yeah," I said. "Me too."

"Sometimes Dad would send me a present in the mail," Paul said. "I mean, it wasn't my birthday or anything. One time he just sent this great electronic game, and Mom saw it and got really mad. She took it and mailed it right back to him. She said I needed other things like shoes and stuff and she didn't have enough money to get them. And when Dad's package came, it made her mad at Dad, I guess."

"But, if you *needed* stuff, how come she was mad when you *got* stuff?"

"I think because she thought it was the *wrong* stuff," he said, moving his shoulders up like he didn't know for sure.

I tried to think if there was anything I really *needed*. I had clothes, and a warm house, and good food that my mom made. I had Pete, my best friend, and there was good ol' Max, and Gram and everybody. I couldn't think of a single thing I needed that I didn't have.

Before long everybody else got there and Paul and I got to help put the food on the table. It smelled so good and we were so hungry we could hardly sit through grace. Everybody ate and talked and laughed about things. I was glad it was Christmas.

We opened our presents and everybody liked what everybody got 'em. Especially my Uncle Allan. He got new slippers from Sis and me and a new robe from Gram. He put them on as soon as he opened them and he wore them the rest of the day.

Later that night we were sitting by the tree, just Sis and Mom and Bill and me. Everybody else had gone home. We only had the tree lights on and the whole room looked soft and pretty. Mom sighed like she was real tired. I snuggled up next to her and she put her arm around me.

"I've never had a three-day Christmas before," I said, trying not to yawn. "It wears you out!"

Mom laughed a little bit. "I'll say it does. Just think how good we'll be at three-day Christmases next year." Then she asked, "How do you feel about all your new families?"

"They're OK, I guess," I said. "But I'll be glad when I know who some of them are." Then I asked a scary question, "Do I have to give Dad's gift back to him?"

She looked at me really funny, "Why would you have to do that?"

"I know it made you mad, and I don't want you to be mad anymore."

"Did you hear me talking to Gram this afternoon?" she asked. I just nodded. "Then I owe you an apology for what you heard," she said. "I was wrong to be angry about his gift, Chip. I was jealous because I couldn't get you something just as nice. Will you forgive me?"

"Oh, Mom," I said, hugging her tight, "I just want you to be happy. I thought about everything today. We got a nice house and clothes to wear, and you cook good. And you love me a whole bunch. That's all I need."

Chapter Six
But What Do I Call Him?

Not very long after Christmas, Mom and Bill got married. I only went to one wedding before, when I was just a little kid. But I got to be *in* this one.

Everybody was all dressed up. Sis had a new dress and flowers in her hair. Gram had a real pretty dress on, too, with a big flower on her shoulder. I had to wear a suit and a cardboard shirt. I took it off right after the wedding.

Mom looked prettier than I ever remember seeing her before. And she looked so happy. I want my mom to be happy. The wedding was real nice with music from a guitar and a flute and all. Then we all went into the other room and Mom and Bill cut up the cake they had. Mom tried to put some in Bill's mouth and got it all over his face. It was funny watching him trying to get all the frosting off. We had a good time.

Before long they changed their clothes and went away for a couple of days on a honeymoon. Sis and I stayed with Gram. But what was really fun was that after a few days Mom and Bill came back and took Sis and me with 'em on our *own* honeymoon. I'd never been on a honeymoon before! We went camping in the mountains and had a great time.

There was only one thing wrong. I didn't know what to call Bill now. Sis called him "Daddy." I couldn't call him that. I was too big. And besides, he *wasn't* my dad. It took me a while, but I worked up enough courage and finally asked him.

"What do you want to call me?" he asked.

"I don't know. Bill, I guess."

"OK," he said, nodding, "that's my name. It should work out fine." Then he grinned and sort of socked me in the arm. We fooled around a couple of minutes. Then he said, "I'd sure like us to be friends, Chip. And friends need to be honest with each other. If there's ever something bothering you, you tell me and we'll talk. OK?"

I dug my shoe into the dirt and uncovered a rock just right for skipping. I told him OK, but I wished my real dad was with me instead. I picked up the rock and threw it as far as I could across the lake.

Chapter Seven
He Can't Tell Me What to Do!

Everybody was settled down after the wedding. Bill was really living with us. Some days that was OK. Some days I didn't like it very much. He was nice and all that, but he didn't do things the way I was used to. He didn't do things like Dad did. I missed my real dad.

One afternoon I was going over to Pete's to play ball till dinner.

"Have you finished your homework, Chip?" Bill asked, putting his jacket in the closet.

"Almost," I said, shoving my mitt down hard on my hand. I was gonna be late.

"What do you have left to do?"

"About six math problems. Easy ones."

"You finish them first, then you can play ball," he said. He picked up the newspaper and unfolded it. I watched him sit down in his big chair and I made a face when he couldn't see.

"I want to play ball *now*. We have to eat pretty soon, and then it'll be dark. I can do the math later, after dinner."

"You do your homework first, Son. That's the rule here."

"I'm not your son!" I yelled at him. "You're not my father! And you can't tell me what to do!"

Bill laid the paper in his lap. "Come stand over here," he said, and I figured I'd better stand where he said. I never yelled at a grown-up before and I figured I was really gonna get it now.

"Chip," he said, "you're right about one thing. I'm not your father. You already have a father and I have no intention of trying to take his place. But we are living together now as a family, and you are going to have to listen to me just like you listen to your mom." I couldn't look at Bill's face. I wished I could be far away.

"Sometimes," he said, "things we do will be fun and we'll have good times like when we were camping. Other times—like right now—I'll have to ask you to do things you don't like. But you will have to do them anyway." I looked at him kinda quick, and he put his arm around my shoulders. "I'll try to be as fair as I can, because I really care about you."

I looked at him for a minute. "Bill," I said, trying not to cry, "I didn't mean to yell at you."

"It's OK," he said, pulling me closer in a kinda rough hug. "I know some things are pretty confusing for you right now. But if we all just hang in there, we'll learn. It'll get better before long if we all really try."

"I want to try," I said. "I really want to try."

Chapter Eight
It's My Room!

Things went along pretty good for a while. It was almost time for summer vacation. One night after dinner we were all sitting around the table and Mom said, "Bill and I have something we'd like to talk to you about." It sounded sort of serious.

Bill said, "You kids know I have a boy of my own. He's just a year younger than you, Chip. Some things have changed and he will be coming to live with us."

"He could play ball with you and Pete," Mom said, smiling at me. "It might be kind of nice to have a brother around. What do you think?"

A brother? Just like that? A brother a year younger than me? It might be OK to have somebody besides Sis to play with sometimes, but what if he's a nurd? What if he doesn't fit in with my friends? What if I don't like him?

"Where's he gonna sleep?" I asked, looking at the crumpled napkin in my hand.

"We were hoping you would share your room with him," Mom said.

"*My* room?" I hollered. "Why can't he have his own room? I don't want anybody in my room. It's *my room!*"

I got up from the table so fast I knocked my chair over. But I was so mad I didn't even stop to pick it up. I just ran up the stairs as fast as I could. I even beat Max to the top.

I slammed the door behind me so hard the pictures on my wall jumped crooked. I thought for sure Mom or Bill would come up the stairs and holler at me for slamming the door, but it just stayed quiet. I was all alone in my room—me and Max.

I flopped on my bed and started looking around. I liked my room. I had my bed and a dresser and my desk with a chair. It was a nice room. I put my hands behind my head and started to think.

It's not fair for me to have to share my room with anybody. I was here first. I stared at the ceiling for a long time just thinking about how I didn't like things the way they were—not any more. I fell asleep wishing things could be the way they used to be before our old divorce.

Chapter Nine
My Brother Mickey

When I woke up the next morning somebody had snuck my shoes off and covered me up with one of Gram's big old quilts. I rolled over and looked out the window. The sun was shining and the wind was pushing the clouds around. It was Saturday!

Pete and I both had new kites and it looked like we'd picked a great day to fly 'em.

I was halfway through my breakfast when the back door banged shut and I heard Bill coming into the kitchen. "Chip," Bill said. I looked up and there he was, standing beside his dad. A skinny kid with blond hair and freckles. "This is Mickey." My new brother! He was *here* already and I didn't have anything to say about it.

We just looked at each other for a minute. He looked OK but something inside me didn't want to like him.

"I gotta go," I said, pushing my chair away from the table. "Pete and me are gonna fly kites today."

Mickey didn't say anything, but his eyes looked real sad. I picked up my jacket and my kite real quick and walked over to the back door. I looked back at Mickey and then pushed open the door and ran down the walk.

I kept running almost all the way to Pete's house. Here it was Saturday. Beautiful Saturday, and I had a new kite to fly. But all I could think about was that sad look on Mickey's face. I wasn't even a little bit nice to him. It didn't feel good being mean.

When I got to Pete's house he grabbed his new kite and we walked together just a little way before I stopped. "We gotta go back to my house," I said, starting to run. "I forgot something."

When we got there I pushed open the back door. Mickey was sitting at the table with Mom and Bill, eating some toast.

"You know how to fly a kite?" I asked him. He nodded his head up and down. "Wanna come?"

He never said. He just grabbed his jacket and ran out the back door with us. But he was grinning.

Chapter Ten
Makin' Changes

Mickey wasn't as big as Pete or me but he could run fast and he was a pretty good kite flier. We went over to Pete's house and his mom made sandwiches for us to take back to the park. We ate sandwiches and apples and talked about stuff.

Mickey was from another city and he said his mom put him on the plane real early that morning so Bill could pick him up at the airport. He looked real sad when he talked about his mom. He didn't say so, but I could tell he missed her a lot.

We played some catch and climbed some trees and then it was time to go home. After we took Pete to his house we walked back to my house. We kicked stones and made a lot of noise together. It was kinda fun having somebody else along.

After dinner we all moved furniture around in my room so we could fit another bed in. Mom and Bill put almost everything where I said it should go.

And I got to help move things, even the beds. When we got all finished, my room sure looked different. It'll be a while before I get used to it like this.

Mickey and me got ready for bed and Mom came in to say good night. She walked over to my bed like always and leaned down to kiss my cheek. She smiled at me, then instead of turning off the light and closing the door like always, she walked over to Mickey's bed and kissed *him* good night, too. My mom! I didn't like that at all. She was *my* mom, not his. He moves in and takes my room and changes my life all around. He gets to live with his dad and now he's gonna take *my mom*! What's left for me?

"Mom," I said, as she got to the door.

"Uh-huh?" she said, turning the light out.

"Can you come here?"

She walked back over to my bed and bent down again. "Mom," I said in a quiet voice Mickey couldn't hear, "do you love me?"

She hugged me real tight. "I'll always love you, honey," she said. "You know I will."

"I know," I said. "I just wanted to hear you say it."

I lay in bed and thought about all the things that had happened in this one day. I got to fly kites and play catch in the park. I fixed my room around all different. And I got a new brother, a stepbrother. And my mom told me she will always love me.

Chapter Eleven
Dumb or Different?

Mickey was living with us alright. Every morning when we were getting ready for school he was standing right where I wanted to stand. If I wanted to brush my teeth, he was using the sink. If I wanted something out of the closet, he was there first. And every towel I got was already wet 'cause he used 'em all first! He was really getting on my nerves.

One day I was telling Gram all the bad stuff about Mickey. "He thinks his dumb old junk box is the greatest thing in the whole world. You should see it, Gram, it's nothin' but junk—an old piece of string, a couple of bottle caps, a rock with sparkly stuff in it—just *junk*. That kid is really dumb!"

"Dumb or *different*?" Gram asked. She tied a knot in the end of some thread and started sewing again.

"I think he's just dumb," I said. Boy, if she only knew him.

All the way home I thought about "dumb or different." I got to wondering if I look dumb sometimes. Like my collection of banks. I don't even keep money in them; I just like banks.

I thought about one time when I stayed over at Pete's house and I was the only one at the dinner table waiting to say grace before we ate. I found out they don't say grace. At my house *everybody* says grace. It made me feel dumb. But I'm not—I'm just different.

Mickey was sitting on the steps with his junk box when I got home. I sat down on the steps, too.

"Whatcha doin'?" I asked.

"Nothin.' "

"What's that?" I asked, pointing to an old brown thing that looked like a button. Mickey picked it up and turned it over and over in his hand.

"It's a button."

"How come you keep a button?"

"It's a button off my gramma's coat." He looked at it. "My gramma died last year."

Mickey looked real sad. I thought about how much I'd miss my Gram if she died. "Is all that stuff like the button?" I asked him. "I mean, do you have a reason for keepin' it?"

Mickey nodded his head, then he looked at me for a minute. "You wanna know some reasons?"

"Yeah," I said. And then Mickey told me about the stuff in his junk box. He had two pop-bottle caps he got at an important baseball game Bill took him to once. And he still has the string that was wrapped around a package his dad sent him when he went to another country as a soldier. It's not regular string.

I found out why he kept all that stuff—it *meant* something to him. I found out something else. Mickey's not dumb, just different than me. Isn't that funny? It took a box full of special junk to teach me about being different.

Chapter Twelve
Do I Hear Yelling?

A couple days later Mickey and I were getting ready for bed. Mom and Bill were in the living room downstairs, and Sis was already asleep. I just started buttoning my pajamas when I thought I heard a loud voice. I stopped and listened. I heard it again. It was Mom and Bill! They were talking awful loud to each other. And worse yet, they sounded angry.

I looked over at Mickey and he looked like I felt inside. *Scared.* We both snuck out of the room and stood by the top of the stairs. Yep! They were yelling alright. About money or something.

I finally got into bed, but I couldn't sleep. I stared at the ceiling and watched the lights move across when cars went by outside. I remembered when my dad left. The lights on his car made patterns across the ceiling that night, too. It started me wondering about some things.

The house was quiet now. Mom and Bill weren't yelling anymore. But I'd never heard them mad at each other before. I'd never heard them argue—until tonight. Don't they love each other anymore? Are *they* going to get divorced? I felt scared all night.

The next day I went downstairs for breakfast. I felt tired and all mixed-up inside—mad and scared and mixed-up. Mom smiled at me when I came in the kitchen. "You look tired, honey," she said, hugging me. "You feeling alright?"

"I'm OK," I said, squeezing in by the table. Mickey was eating his cereal. He just looked at me over a spoonful of Cheerios. I poured some milk on my cereal, but when I reached for the sugar bowl I knocked over the milk pitcher. The next thing I knew there was milk and broken pottery all over the floor. Mom turned around with a surprised look on her face.

"Aren't you gonna yell at me?" I asked. I sounded mad.

"Why should I yell at you, Chip?" Mom said, kinda quiet. "It was an accident, wasn't it?"

"Yeah," I said, "but you yelled at Bill last night. I heard you . . . " I didn't mean to say that. I felt awful.

Mom dried her hands on the little towel that hung on the oven door. Then she came and crouched down between me and Mickey. The milk was still all over the floor. She put her arms around our shoulders and said, "I didn't think you boys heard us last night. I'm sorry you did. But I want to tell you something.

"You boys have both been through a divorce, and I would guess that when you heard Bill and me arguing last night you were afraid that we would get divorced too. Right?"

I looked at Mickey. His eyes and mouth were open wide. "How'd you know that?" Mickey asked Mom.

"Because most folks feel that people argue because they don't love each other."

"You and Dad argued a lot and then you got divorced," I said.

"That's right. But the arguing isn't what made the divorce happen. Didn't you and Pete have an argument just last week?" I nodded. We sure did. "Are you still friends?"

"Sure we are," I said. "Pete's my best friend."

"And best friends argue sometimes. It's a way of working things out, and once you are able to settle things it makes you understand each other even better."

"You mean," Mickey asked, "that you and my dad can argue and yell and you can still love each other just the same—like Chip and me do with our friends?"

"Just like that," Mom said, nodding her head up and down. "Just because two people love each other doesn't mean they agree on everything."

"But you and Dad argued and you got a divorce. I don't understand how this is different."

"When people argue it doesn't always mean they're unhappy inside," Mom said. "Bill and I do lots of things differently, and sometimes we both think our way is the right way. That's when we have to work out the differences and come to an agreement. And sometimes we'll get into an argument in the process. But we love each other, so we work it out."

"Then sometimes," Mickey said slowly, thinking it all out, "sometimes arguing can be OK, if people are really trying to work out stuff."

"And," I added, "getting mad at each other is just a part of people living together."

"I think you boys understand now," Mom said, smiling. "It's *because we love each other* we work through the bad things to make things good again."

Chapter Thirteen
Always

One Saturday my real dad and I got to spend the whole day together. We had a good time. We went to an airplane museum in the park and got to see all kinds of planes. Some of them were even older than Dad. I told him I didn't think anything was older than he was, and he laughed. It was nice to laugh with my dad again.

"How's everything going at home?" Dad asked while we were spreading mustard on some hotdogs later on.

"OK, I guess," I said, dipping into the big jar for some relish.

"You getting along OK with Bill?"

I felt kinda funny talking about Bill with my real dad. I mean, like I was sorta cheating Dad or something. "We get along OK," I said, but I didn't look at his eyes.

We finished our hotdogs while we walked over to another place in the park where they have real trains—engines and everything—and you can crawl around on them and nobody yells at you to get off. There was one old passenger car that was fixed up just like the trains they used to run when the West was still full of cowboys and Indians. It was really neat!

"Dad," I said, hanging from one of the metal bars on the side of the train, "do you love me?"

He looked up at me with a kinda funny smile and said, "Of course I love you. You're my boy."

"Dad," I said, looking through the window into the train.

"Yeah?"

"Would you be mad if I called Bill 'Dad'? I mean, sometimes it feels like he's my dad."

My dad didn't say anything. I turned around to see what he was doing. He was walking away from me real slow. I jumped down from the train and ran after him.

"Dad?" I asked. He didn't answer me. "Dad, are you mad at me? I won't call him 'Dad' if you don't want me to. Honest."

He stopped walking and turned around. I watched his eyes when he looked at me but I couldn't tell what was wrong. I felt scared inside.

"Dad," I asked, "what's the matter?"

"I've been thinking some things through," he said. "You took me by surprise just now. I never thought about you calling somebody else 'Dad' and I didn't know how to answer." He started walking slow again, so I walked with him.

"My very first thoughts," he said, "were that you only have *one* dad—me. That made me want to say, 'No, don't call him Dad.' But then I started to think about what it must be like to live with him like you do, and I realized something. What you call somebody else can't change the facts. I'm still your dad and I always will be."

He smiled at me a little, then he scooped me up onto his shoulders. I hung onto his forehead while he ran across the grass under the trees. I grabbed a low branch and held on, laughing. Dad was laughing with me.

He came back to where I was and flopped down on the grass below me. I dropped out of the branches and landed right beside him.

"I love you, Son. I would never be mad at you for liking Bill or calling him 'Dad,' if that's what you want to call him." He sat up and looked at me real hard. "Nothing will ever change the way I feel about you." Then he looked right in my eyes and said, "You will always be my son."

Chapter Fourteen
Can I Really Trust You?

"**H**ey, Chip, Mickey!" Bill whispered kinda loud. "You awake?" Everything sounded muffled under my warm covers.

"I am now," I said, trying to open my eyes, "well, almost."

It was still real early in the morning, and it was Saturday. "How come you're waking us up this early on *Saturday?*"

"To find out if you and Mickey want to do some fishing with me today."

"FISHING!?" we yelled at the same time. We were sitting up, wide awake now. I don't think I ever moved so fast to get my clothes on. I pulled my T-shirt on right over my pajamas. I had to take it off again to get it right.

We didn't eat breakfast at home. Bill took us to a place and let us get pancakes and eggs for breakfast so Mom wouldn't have to get up so early to cook. It was still cold outside when we got back in the car. Bill started driving to the beach and Mickey and me saw the sunrise. The whole sky was red and there weren't any other cars on the roads hardly at all.

When we got to the ocean I thought we were going to fish from the pier like I did with my real dad before. It was a lot of fun. We even caught some fish. But Bill didn't drive to the pier. Instead he took us to a place in the marina where they keep the boats. And we got to go way out on the ocean on a big boat to fish for the whole day! I'd never been on such a big boat before. This was a for-real fishing boat with sailors and everything. Bill said the guy that drove the boat was a friend of his, so we got to meet him and see what the captain's cabin looked like.

The wind was cold at first but after the sun had been up for a little while the whole day got warm and nice. Big seagulls flew around the boat all day. I guess they were hoping we'd drop some of our fish so they could eat them. I leaned on my elbows at the railing and held on tight to my pole. The boat moved back and forth just a little bit when the waves made us roll around. I guess it was just about a perfect day.

Bill and Mickey and me laughed and fished and ate sandwiches until the sun was about ready to go down. The captain started the engines again for the last time that day and turned us back to the marina. We were really sad that it couldn't go on forever.

Bill talked and told us some funny stories on the way home. Mickey laughed and was having a good time with his dad. I was too, but inside I was wishing I could have been with *my* real dad like Mickey.

I watched Bill while he was driving back home. He had a nice face. He was a nice person to be with. I guess I could see why Mom liked him so much. And I wanted to like him too. But I was scared.

What if I got to really likin' Bill? Then what if he decided to leave us? I remember feeling so sad when my dad left. And I don't *ever* want to feel that sad again.

Bill turned the car into the driveway. We all went into the house and Mickey and I got to show Mom all the neat fish we caught. I guess Mickey caught the longest one, but I caught the fattest one for sure. We sat out in the backyard cleaning them. (Mom said we couldn't clean 'em in the house.)

After they were all cleaned, Mickey and I were helping Mom wrap 'em all up for the freezer, except for two for dinner. Mickey was telling her all the stuff we did on the boat and things.

"What was your favorite part?" Mom asked me finally. "I haven't heard very much from you at all so far. Did you have a good time?"

"Yeah," I said, squeezing the tin foil around one of the fish. "I had a great time." She looked at me kinda long. I guess I didn't sound very much like I'd had a good time.

Mickey went upstairs to take his bath first (he needed one worse than I did anyway). Mom looked at me again and put her arm around my shoulders. "You want to talk about it?"

"I don't know," I said. "I don't know what to say."

"Did you and Bill have a disagreement?" she asked.

"Huh-uh," I said, shaking my head. "We really had a great time."

"Then what's wrong, honey?"

"I guess . . . I'm kinda . . . scared," I said in a little voice.

"Scared of Bill?"

"Huh-uh." I shook my head again. "He's real nice to me."

"Then what are you scared of? I don't understand." Mom looked confused.

"I don't understand either," I said. "I really like Bill, but every time I feel like I like him I get scared."

Mom picked up the fish and opened the freezer door. She started stacking them inside. "I wonder," she said, "if you're just having a hard time learning how to trust somebody again."

I thought about that. I wanted to trust Bill, but I wasn't sure I did. "I don't know," I said, handing her the last fish.

"Honey," she said, looking straight at my eyes, "when you have trusted someone who's let you down, it's hard to trust again. After our divorce I had to learn to trust people all over again, too."

"I thought you always trusted people, Mom."

"I acted like I did, but down inside I was scared just like you are. I didn't believe anybody. I didn't let myself love anybody for a long time."

"But you *married* Bill. Don't you trust him?"

"Yes," Mom said, "but I dated Bill a very long time before I believed I could really trust him, before I knew he meant what he was saying. And the longer I know him, the more sure I am that he really is the kind of person we think he is. I am learning to trust him more every day."

"How come it's so hard to believe somebody who never even lied to us?"

"Because we've been hurt. So we just keep people far enough away to keep from getting hurt again. We try to stop the love."

"Like Monopoly?" I asked.

"Monopoly?" Mom said, looking very confused.

"Yeah. I love to play Monopoly but I hate to lose. So sometimes I don't even ask my friends to play 'cause I don't want to lose again."

"You're right," Mom said, "there's a lot of risk involved in things like that."

"Lots of things are like that," I said, sort of thinking out loud. "I like to do wheelies, but sometimes I get too far back and the whole bike falls over on me. And I like to sit by Becky Anderson in my class sometimes, but not too much, 'cause I don't want her to tell me to go away."

Mom covered a grin with her hand, but she pulled it away again real quick and went over to the sink to wash the fishy smell off.

"How come the stuff we like has to have a part that hurts?" I asked.

"I guess life is just like that," Mom said, scrubbing her hands another time. "All the things in life that are important involve risks. Like holding a job or running for class president or learning to play an instrument well or playing sports—or loving somebody." She dried her hands and hugged me tight. "Chip, we have to take risks if we want our lives to count."

"I guess you're right, Mom," I said, hugging her back. "I want to trust Bill. I really do. And I'm gonna try—even if it hurts."

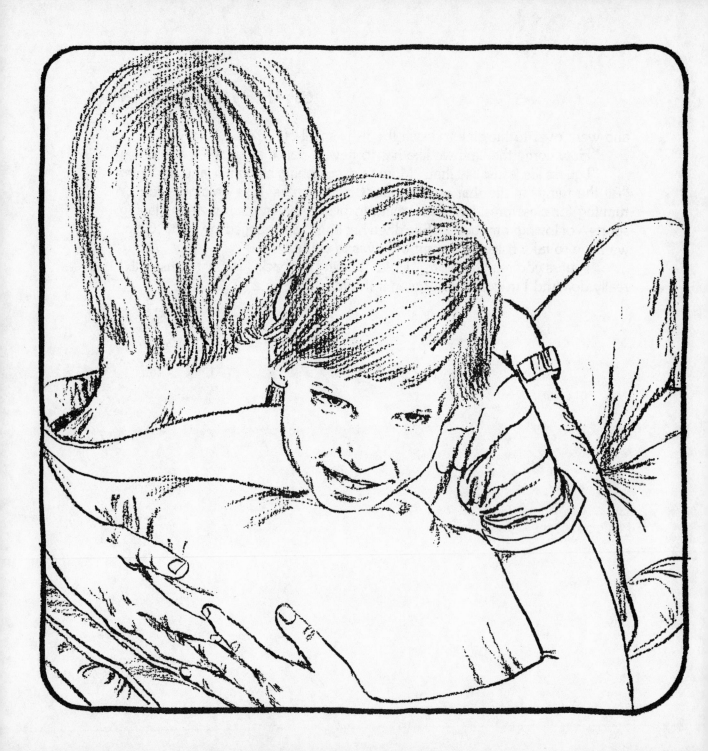

Chapter Fifteen
I'm Gonna Try

After I took my bath we had dinner. Mom fixed some of the fish we caught. They were OK, I guess, if you like fish. I sure like catching 'em, but I'm not crazy about eating them. Mom says I'll probably really *love* fish by the time we get through eating all the ones we caught today.

I was really tired, so I started upstairs to bed. I looked back in the living room. Bill was just getting his shoes off so he could read the paper comfortable. His face was all sunburned and he looked sort of tired around his eyes. I went back down the stairs and stood next to his chair for a minute.

"Bill?"

"Yeah?" he said, looking up at me.

"Thanks. It was a neat day."

He smiled real wide and nodded his head up and down. "Yeah," he said, "I had a good time, too. We'll have to do it again."

"I . . . " the words stuck in my throat and I couldn't look at his eyes. "You're OK, for a stepdad."

He sat up straight in his chair. "I'm really glad you think so, young man," he said. "You're not bad yourself." I reached around his neck and gave him a real quick hug. Then as fast as I could, I ran upstairs.

Chapter Sixteen
A Real Family?

I was sitting in church one morning between Mom and Bill and I was listening to the story of Joseph. He was a guy who lived a long time ago and had a lot of brothers who were really mean to him. In fact, they sold him away to a far country to be a SLAVE! And while he was there some lady said some lies about him and he ended up in jail for a long time—and he hadn't even done anything!

Well, pretty soon God came along and made some real changes in Joseph's life. He got him out of jail and made him the most important person in the whole land of Egypt except for the Pharaoh. And then Joseph got a chance to get even with his mean old brothers. But instead of hurting them back for all the things they'd done to him before, Joseph said, "You meant it for bad, but God meant it for good."

I got to thinking on the way home, when we got our divorce and then Bill married my mom, I thought only bad things could come out of all that. But Bill has lived at our house for a long time now. I'm used to having him and Mickey around. Sometimes I think I might even miss Mickey if he moved away. (Other times I don't think so.) He still gets on my nerves sometimes, but I guess that's just part of living together. I don't think I know anybody who does *everything* the way I like.

Mickey and me are becoming good friends, and Bill is easy to talk to, most of the time. I like some of the changes, too, like having Bill around when I need some help on my bike, or knowing that he and Mom are just in the next room when the wind is howling outside my window. And Mom seems so happy now. That's the best part of all.

So I was thinking, even though the divorce was a sad thing for us to go through, and even though there's been a lot of changing, maybe God is making good things out of it for us—just like He did for Joseph.

A Special Note
to Parents and Stepparents

This little book is NOT a statement on divorce or remarriage. My hope is that it will reach and help youngsters who find themselves in families where, through death or divorce, there is a stepparent in their lives.

Children of these families face some difficult adjustments. The issues discussed here were chosen in an attempt to broaden your understanding of children's common fears about stepparents and stepfamilies. If you read this book to or along with your child, it may create a basis for some productive and rewarding sharing.

The child in this book adjusts neatly and quickly to the new people and situations in his life. Your child may not be so quick to respond. Love doesn't happen accidentally. It's not something we can legislate or demand. Love is *earned* through good hard work.

As the Child's Natural Parent

Try to give your child a chance to adjust to the idea of remarriage *before* the wedding. Prepare him (or her) for the changes that will be taking place by telling the child honestly, "We may have some problems, but we'll work them out together as we go along."

You may find it difficult to share responsibilities that have been exclusively yours for a while. Your new mate's methods of doing things and his (or her) priorities will probably not be exactly the same as yours, and you may not want to accept a new way of doing things. But it's worth all the hard work it takes to become a team, so keep trying.

Consistency is needed from **both** *you and your mate.* Talk through your expectations of behavior and approaches to discipline. You'll both need a flexible attitude and an honest and open approach to your partner's ideas and convictions. Be willing to compromise—both of you.

Become a continual learner. Be eager to discover new things about your mate and your family. As you learn more about each of them you will be able to choose successful methods of dealing with family problems.

As a Stepparent

You will probably find yourself in the center of a family that has done a lot of growing up without you. Each member of that family comes equipped with a personal package of memories, confusion, fear and prejudice. Your child is bringing old wounds into the new family. Give him (or her) time. Don't expect healing overnight.

Face facts: a new family is just beginning. Give everybody a chance to "settle in" and get adjusted to the new way of life remarriage creates before attempting any major changes. Pay close attention to your timing. It can make all the difference in the world.

Learning to trust people outside the family is one of the big-time lessons of childhood. Your child has already gone through major changes adjusting to a single-parent family. Remarriage requires further adjustments to yet another new situation—the replacing of shattered trust with a very slowly growing new security.

It shouldn't be surprising then that you may be met with a great deal of resistance in place of the open arms you'd hoped might greet you. Don't take it personally. It is to be expected.

As you begin to move into the family you may sense a great deal of resentment or jealousy from the child. In adjusting to a single-parent family, the child has had to make some major changes. Remarriage presents a real threat to a newly-established pattern of security for him (or her). But threats subside in safe surroundings.

Draw liberally from the natural parent's knowledge of the child. Are reactions you are now seeing the child's usual reactions to situations? Or is he (or she) reacting to the divorce, or showing a dislike for you? Consult with the person who should know the child best—your new mate.

Be willing to compromise with your mate on how the child will be raised. Be an involved party in the discipline or you may build a reputation of an impotent, second-class adult within your own home. Discipline can and should be a *joint* responsibility with each supporting the other—consistently.

He may be confused about what to call you. Let it be the child's choice based on personal needs. And don't let titles bother you. No matter what your child calls you, your position in the family is unchangeable. Names don't change the facts. Let the child choose; and don't feel hurt by his or her candid comments. Openness with this issue may prepare the way for real honesty in other areas.

Your child may argue, "You're not my dad (or mother). You can't tell me what to do!" This attitude needs to be dealt with. The first part of the statement is true. You need to remind the child that you are aware of your relationship. But the second thought needs to be corrected. Although you are not the natural parent it's important that the child recognizes you as a respected member of the family who does, indeed, have a say in how he (or she) will be raised.

Try to remain neutral rather than taking a stand against the absent parent. Running him (or her) down only backfires on *you* before long. Remind the child, "I'm not trying to take your mother's (or father's) place. I just want to be friends with you."

Set a good example of acceptance. The key to acceptance is to get rid of expectations. If you enter your new family expecting things to be a certain way you are bound to be disappointed. People are unique. That's one of the elements that keeps life interesting. Throw out any "role expectations" you may be harboring by mentally starting off each member of the family with a "clean slate." Look at your family as a collection of totally unique, interesting people about whom you want to learn all you can.

Both Parents

You may find that your child may be dealing with the fear of losing again. Someone your child loved very much is no longer there. Adjusting to a new parent involves risking another loss. He (or she) may purposely withhold loyalty in the face of such a great fear. Your child needs assurance. Consistency is the visible promise of your continued dependability. Don't give up hope if you are making an effort by yourself for a long time. Your consistent example *will* have returns in your child's life.

The fear of betraying the natural parent, whether living or not, may be causing your child a great deal of concern. In the case of divorce, most children dream about their estranged parents getting back together again. Remarriage shatters their hopes and they may be angry with you both for spoiling their dream.

In a child's mind it may seem that if he likes the new adult he is rejecting the missing parent. Your acceptance of the child's absent parent will help assuage his fear of betrayal, and if confirmation from that parent is possible, it can dispel the child's fears of being disloyal.

If the missing parent is struggling with getting his or her own life back in order, the child may feel a need to protect the parent. It is extremely difficult for the child to accept a perfect stranger as someone smarter or better than his own parent, especially if the new person makes the shortcomings of the natural parent obvious. The child may almost dare the stepparent to be a better or nicer person than Dad or Mom, because he doesn't want to admit that his natural parent has failings. So don't be shaken by the child's comparisons to the natural parent. *And above all, don't try to compete!* Teach the child to enjoy each person's uniqueness.

The child may push you to test his and your limits. Although it may not seem so, much of this behavior is subconscious. Take the initiative here. Clear the air. "It must be hard for you," you could say, "to trust a new mom (or dad), hard to believe he (or she) will love you and stay with you. We're going to work hard to make it happen though—no matter how you act—because we want you to have a happy family."

Your child may confront you with unfair expectations for no apparent reason. He or she may be looking for a replacement exactly like the missing parent. You can help the child understand that each person must be accepted *on his (or her) own merit* by continuing to accept those around you. It is the best example you can offer. If he (or she) accuses, "My dad doesn't do that," it is a simple matter to inform the child that, "At *his* house your father makes the rules. At *this* house we make them."

Stepfamilies Have Their Own Unique Difficulties.

Children are opposed to change, especially major change. It is of paramount importance to them to be able to feel that they have some control in their lives by at least knowing what to expect. Change means unpredictability and insecurity to them.

Make your new marriage come first. Just keeping your priorities straight will keep your home operating more smoothly. Making sure your marriage is healthy and in good shape means the kids will have a healthy, happy place to live. It won't take them long to realize that your attention to each other is partly for them.

To grow, children need "safe" environments. You can provide that for them with continued consistency. If your child can depend on you to be honest and real all the time, you will be the steady, dependable person he (or she) had hoped for from the beginning.

Be an incurable listener. Counselors are paid great sums of money to be good listeners. They are helpless to make any changes in the lives they touch, and yet, almost magically, changes occur because their clients are being heard. Listen to your child. He (or she) is working through major difficulties in learning to adjust to new things in the family. Be a good enough friend to hear them out. You'll be so glad you did.

Take the initiative. Old feelings won't just "go away" by themselves. Encourage talk, even though your own scars may make you wish you could just hide the past. It can't be hidden, and talking through our feelings is an *effective* way of learning to live with what we have feared. Closeness with your child can be one of the benefits of being willing to talk about fears, in spite of the pain.

Demonstrate your acceptance of the missing parent. The child is entitled to a personal relationship with the absent parent regardless of what you may think of him (or her). A poor mate can be a good parent.

Make your house a real home by balancing the pleasure with some responsibility, whether the child lives with you or just visits. Establish some realistic goals and work toward them, like learning to live peacefully and respectfully with each other. The result may be that many of the problems in your home become less difficult to live with.

In some cases, no matter how hard you try, love may not develop between the child and the stepparent. But within a sound family structure, a mutual understanding and respect can still be achieved.

Last, but *most* important of all, let me remind you that *any difficulty you may face in your life can be handled with confidence and peace of mind when it is faced in partnership with Almighty God.* His power is yours to draw on. Like Gram says, "Divorce and stepparents and anything else you can think of are things that God deals with all the time. They don't scare Him one bit."

Your comments, questions and suggestions are encouraged and appreciated. I would be delighted to hear from you. Please write in care of Regal Books, P.O. Box 3875, Ventura, CA 93006, or P.O. Box 1073, Yorba Linda, CA 92686.